Devanagari

◉ Suryastra

ISBN: 978-81-903678-8-2

Devanagari - a Hindi alphabet note book

Concept © Suryastra

First Edition 2009
Published by
Suryastra
21A Hauz Khas Village
New Delhi 110016
India

www.suryastra.com

Email: info@suryastra.com

Devanagari   देवनागरी

Devanagari is a script used to write several languages of India and Nepal, including Sanskrit, Hindi, Marathi and Nepali.

Around CE 1200, devanagari, a writing system, emerged from the Sharada script which had its roots in the ancient Brahmi script.

From the late Middle Ages, and especially in modern times, the devanagari script has become the most widely used and associated with Sanskrit and Hindi.

Devanagari is an abugida writing system, as each consonant has an inherent vowel - a, which can be changed with the different vowel signs. Devanagari is written from left to right.

This introduction acts as a stepping stone in recognising the devanagari characters, and helping with the pronunciation of the language.

Acknowledgements

We are grateful to Mohan Rana and Vimlesh Kanti Verma
for their comments,
and Shilpi Pratap for her drawings.

How to use the notebook.

Before starting there is a key to pronunciation.

A Hindi word has been placed in the top of the right hand page beginning with the Devanagari character placed at the top of the left hand page. At the bottom of the page are the equivalent roman alphabets, with an illustration in the centre of the right hand page to ease recognition. Some characters do not start a word, and where this is the case we have left a space for you to write words that use this character.

At the back of the book there is a table of the selected Hindi words with their roman script and English translation.

Following there is a list of the Devanagari vowels and their representative signs used in forming words, and a list of the consonants.

We have tried to select simple words and this book is simply a way to recognise the Devanagari characters and to encourage further learning of Hindi.

Key to pronunciation

There is an 'a' inherent in each consonant, and it is pronounced as 'u' in umbrella.

अ   is pronounced as 'a' in the word affection.

आ   as 'a' in art.

इ   as 'i' in if.

ई   as 'ee' in sweet.

उ   as 'u' in pull.

ऊ   as 'oo' in cool.

ऋ   as 'ri', which is pronounced as 'rishi',

       meaning seer.

ए   as 'a' in aim.

ऐ   as 'a' in ate.

ओ   as 'o' in oat.

औ   as 'o' in orb.

अं   as 'un' in junk.

अः   as the sound of 'uh'.

क्	as 'c' in come.
ख	as the sound of 'kh'.
ग	as 'gu' in gull.
घ	as the sound of 'gh'.
ङ	as 'n' in song.
च	as 'ch' in chuckle.
छ	as the sound of 'chh'.
ज	as 'j' in jungle.
झ	as the sound of 'jh'.
ञ	as 'n' in young.
ट	as 't' in touch.
ठ	as the sound of 'th'.
ड	as 'd' in done.
ढ	as the sound of 'dh'.
ण	as 'n' in tongue.

त   as the sound of 't'.

थ   as 'th' in thumb.

द   as 'th' in the.

ध   as the sound of 'dh'.

न   as 'n' in number.

प   as 'p' in pumpkin.

फ   as the sound of 'ph'.

ब   as 'b' in but.

भ   as the sound of 'bh'.

म   as 'm' in mustard.

य   as 'y' in yearn.

र   as 'r' in rush.

ल   as 'l' in love.

व   as 'v' in verb.

श   as 'sh' in bush.

ष   as the sound of 'shh'.

स   as 's' in subtle.

ह   as 'h' in humble.

क्ष   as the sound of 'ksh'.

त्र   as the sound of 'tr'.

ज्ञ   as the sound of 'gy'.

अ

अ

अ

अनार

anaar

अ

अा

aa

आम

aam

इ

इ

i

इमली

imlee

ਈ

ee

ईंट

eent

उ

U

उंगली

ungli

ऊ

ॐ

ऊन

oon

ऋ

ri

ऋतु

ritu

ए

e

एक

ek

ऐ

ai

ऐनक

ainak

ओ

ओ

ओ

ओस

OS

औ

औ

वU

औरत

aurat

अं

ang

अंगूर

angoor

अः

अः

ah

क

ka

कान

kaan

ख

kha

खरगोश

kharagosh

ग

ga

गमला

gamalaa

घ

gha

घर

ghar

ङं

anga

च

च

cha

चांद

chaand

छ

chha

छतरी

chhataree

ज

ja

जड़

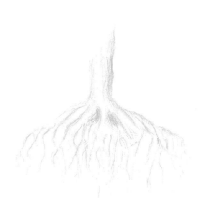

jar

झ

jha

झाड़ू

jhaadoo

अ

अ

yan

ट

ta

टमाटर

tamaatar

ਠ

ਠ

tha

ਠੁੱਡੀ

thuddee

ड

da

डगर

dagar

ढ

dha

ढोल

dhol

ण

na

त

ta

तितली

titalee

थ

थ

tha

थन

than

द

da

दवात

davaat

ध

dha

धनुष

dhanush

न

na

नल

nal

प

pa

पंख

pankh

फ

pha

फूल

phool

ब

ba

बंदर

bandar

भ

bha

भालू

bhaloo

म

ma

माँ

maa

य

ya

युवक

yuvak

र

ra

रवि

ravi

ल

la

लट्टू

lattoo

व

va

वृक्ष

vriksha

श

श

sha

शेर

sher

प

sha

षटकोण

shatkon

स

sa

सांप

saanp

ह

ha

हाथी

haathee

क्ष

ksha

क्ष्मा

kshmaa

त्र

tra

त्रिकोण

trikon

झ

gya

ज्ञान

KNOWLEDGE

gyan

Hindi Script	Roman Script	English Translation
अनार	anaar	pomegranate
आम	aam	mango
इमली	imlee	tamarind
ईंट	eent	brick
उंगली	ungli	finger
ऊन	oon	wool
ऋतु	ritu	season
एक	ek	one
ऐनक	ainak	glasses
ओस	os	dew
औरत	aurat	women
अंगूर	angoor	grape

Hindi Script	Roman Script	English Translation
कान	kaan	ear
खरगोश	kharagosh	rabbit
गमला	gamalaa	plant pot
घर	ghar	home
चांद	chand	moon
छतरी	chhataree	umbrella
जड़	jar	root
झाड़ू	jhadoo	broom
टमाटर	tamaatar	tomato
ठुड्डी	thudee	chin
डगर	dagar	the path
ढोल	dhol	drum

Hindi Script	Roman Script	English Translation
तितली	titalee	butterfly
थन	than	udder
दवात	davaat	ink-pot
धनुष	dhanush	bow
नल	nal	tap
पंख	pankh	feather
फूल	phool	flower
बंदर	bandar	monkey
भालू	bhaloo	bear
माँ	maa	mother
युवक	yuvak	youth
रवि	ravi	sun

Hindi Script	Roman Script	English Translation
लट्टू	lattoo	top
वृक्ष	vriksha	tree
शेर	sher	lion
षटकोण	shatkon	hexagon
सांप	saanp	snake
हाथी	haathee	elephant
क्ष्मा	kshmaa	globe
त्रिकोण	trikon	triangle
ज्ञान	gyaan	knowledge

vowel signs

अ		a
आ	ा	aa
इ	ि	i
ई	ी	ee
उ	ु	u
ऊ	ू	oo
ऋ	ृ	ri

vowel signs

ए	े	e
ऐ	ै	ai
ओ	ो	o
औ	ौ	au
अं	ं	an
अः	ः	ah

consonant characters

क	ka
ख	kha
ग	ga
घ	gha
ङ	unga
च	cha
छ	chha

consonant characters

ज	ja
झ	jha
ञ	yan
ट	ta
ठ	tha
ड	da
ढ	dha

consonant characters

ण	na
त	ta
थ	tha
द	da
ध	dha
न	na
प	pa

consonant characters

फ	pha
ब	ba
भ	bha
म	ma
य	ya
र	ra
ल	la

consonant characters

व	va
श	sha
ष	sha
स	s
ह	ha
क्ष	ksha
त्र	tra
ज्ञ	gya

हिन्दी वर्णमाला

अ	आ	इ	ई	उ
ऊ	ऋ	ए	ऐ	ओ
औ	अं	अः		
क	ख	ग	घ	ङ
च	छ	ज	झ	ञ
ट	ठ	ड	ढ	ण
त	थ	द	ध	न
प	फ	ब	भ	म
य	र	ल	व	
श	ष	स	ह	
क्ष	त्र	ज्ञ		

Hindi Varnamala (Alphabet)